EASIEST 5-FINGER PIANO COLLECTION

Ballads

15 popular ballads
arranged for 5-finger piano

Wise Publications
part of The Music Sales Group
London / New York / Paris / Sydney / Copenhagen / Berlin / Madrid / Tokyo

I HAVE A DREAM

Words & Music by Benny Andersson & Björn Ulvaeus

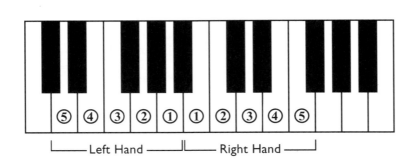

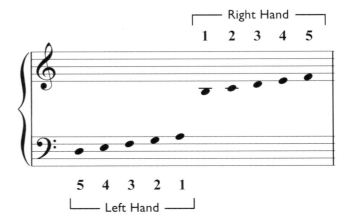

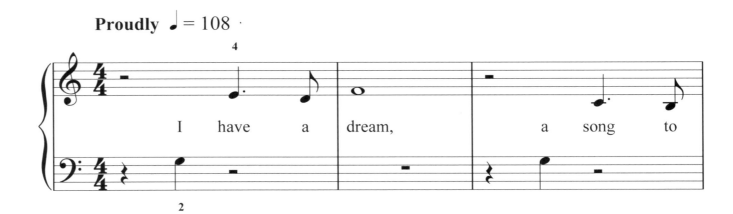

DON'T KNOW WHY

Words & Music by Jesse Harris

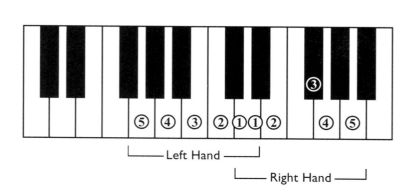

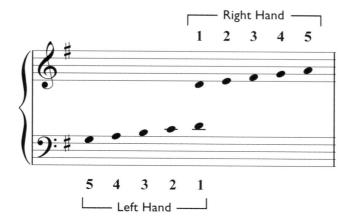

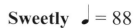

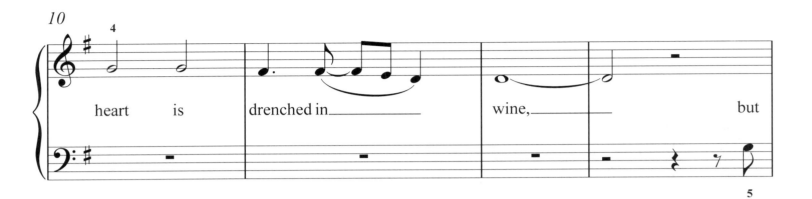

heart is drenched in_____ wine,_____ _____ but

you'll be on my_____ mind for - ev - er.

Some - thing has__ to make__ you run, don't know why_____ I did -

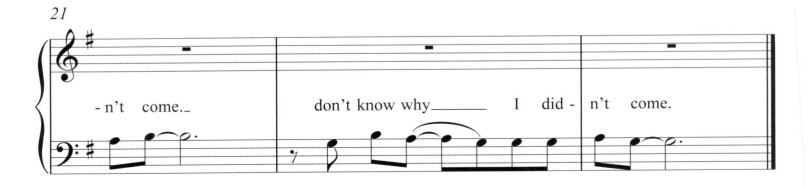

-n't come.__ don't know why_____ I did - n't come.

LET IT BE

Words & Music by John Lennon & Paul McCartney

© Copyright 1970 Sony/ATV Music Publishing (UK) Limited.
All Rights Reserved. International Copyright Secured.

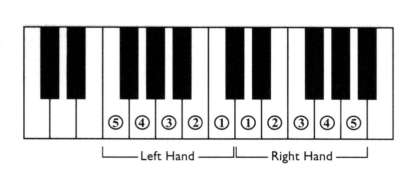

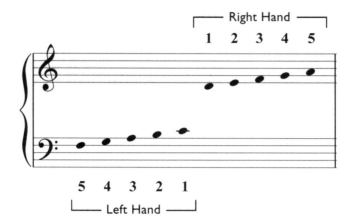

Solemnly ♩ = 116

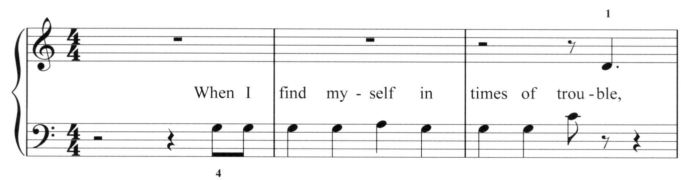

When I find my-self in times of trou-ble,

Moth-er Ma - ry comes to me,___ speak-ing words of

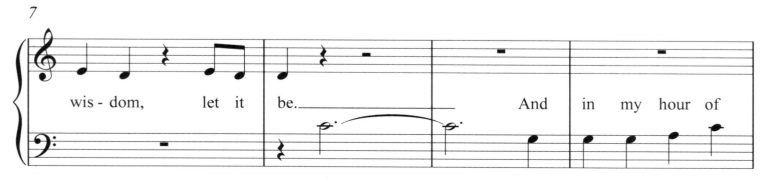

wis-dom, let it be.___ And in my hour of

darkness she is standing right in front of me,___

speak-ing words of wis- dom, let it be.___ Let it

be, let it be, let it be,___ let it be,

whis-per words of wis - dom, let it be.___

ETERNAL FLAME

Words & Music by Susanna Hoffs, Tom Kelly & Billy Steinberg

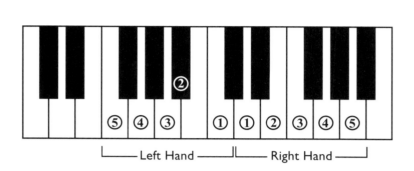

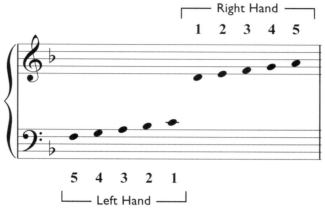

Steadily ♩ = 84

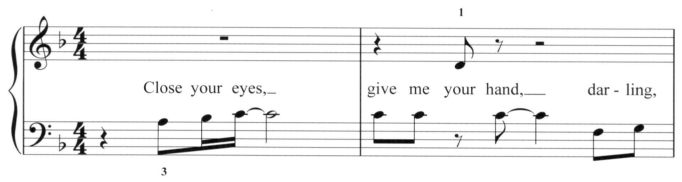

Close your eyes,_ give me your hand,_ dar - ling,

do you feel my heart beat - ing?_ Do you un - der -

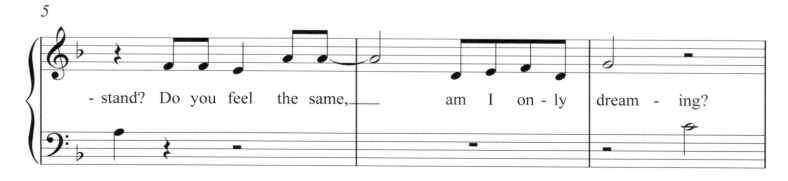

- stand? Do you feel the same,_ am I on - ly dream - ing?

WONDERFUL TONIGHT

Words & Music by Eric Clapton

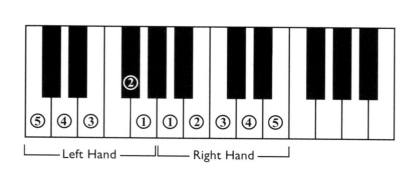

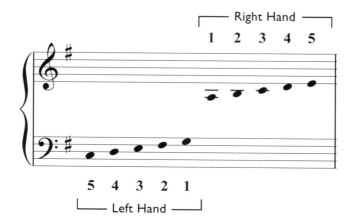

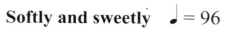

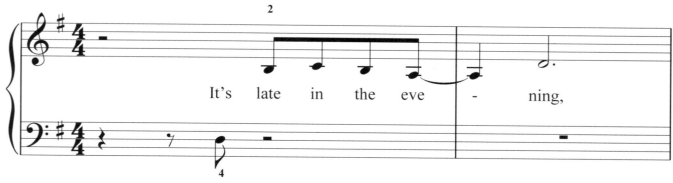

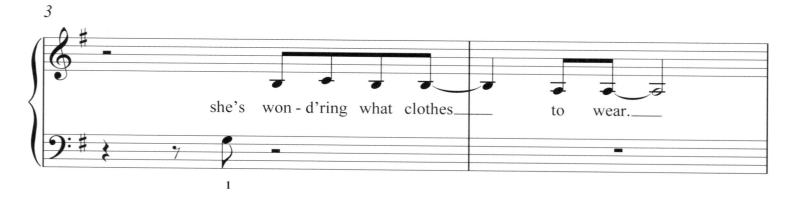

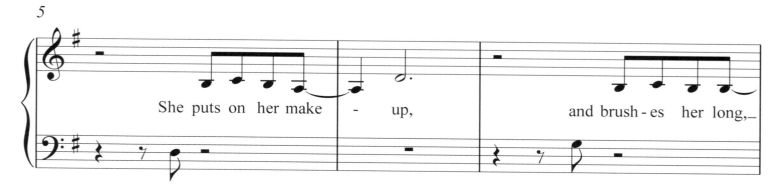

blonde hair.___ And then she asks___ me,

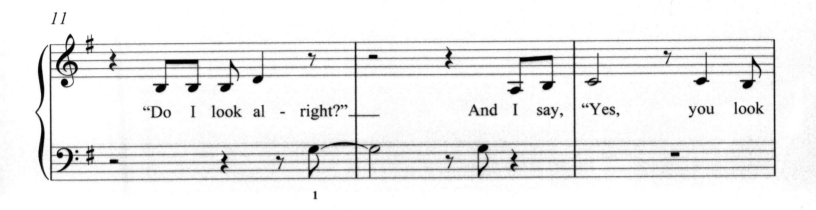

"Do I look al - right?"___ And I say, "Yes, you look

won - der - ful___ to - night." "Oh, my

dar - ling,___ you look won - der - ful___ to-night."

CAN YOU FEEL THE LOVE TONIGHT?

Words by Tim Rice. Music by Elton John.

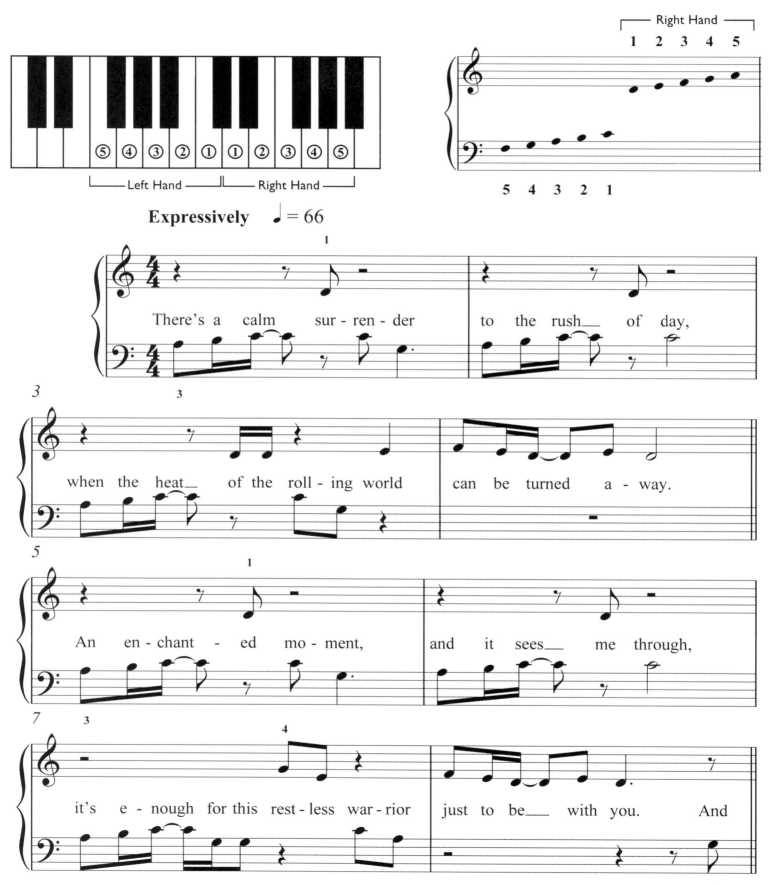

EVERYTIME

Words & Music by Britney Spears & Annette Stamatelatos

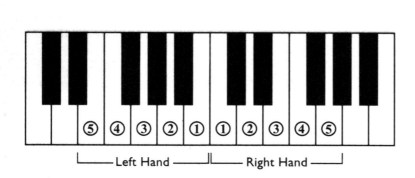

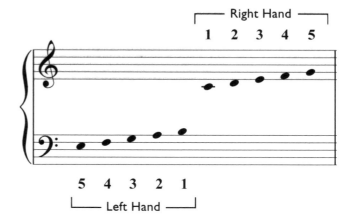

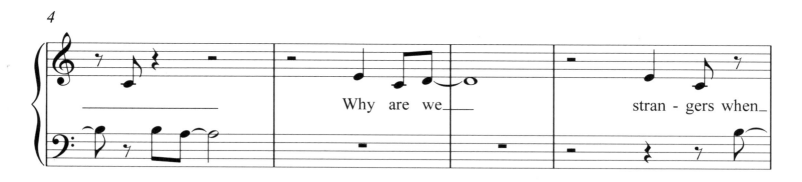

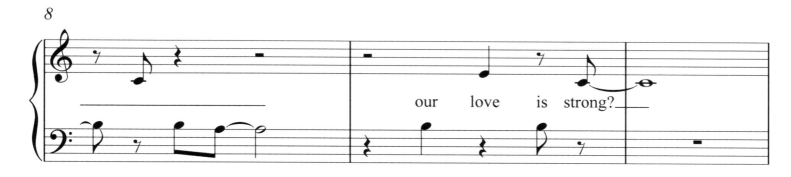

WHAT A WONDERFUL WORLD

Words & Music by George Weiss & Bob Thiele

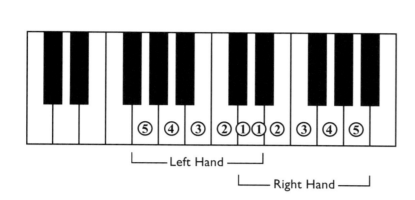

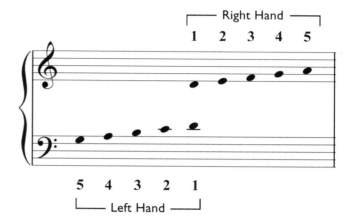

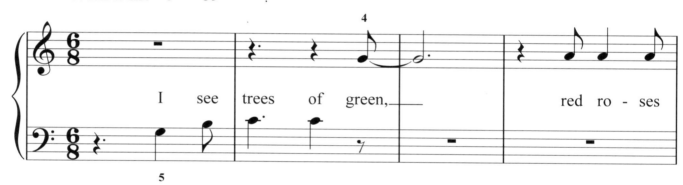

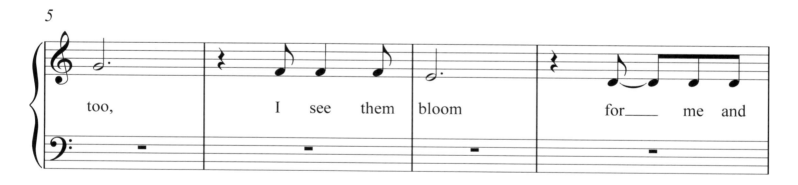

FIX YOU

Words & Music by Guy Berryman, Chris Martin, Jon Buckland & Will Champion

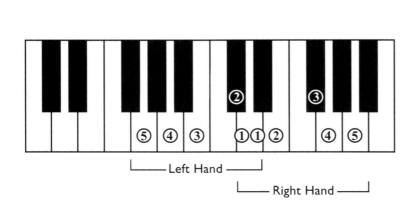

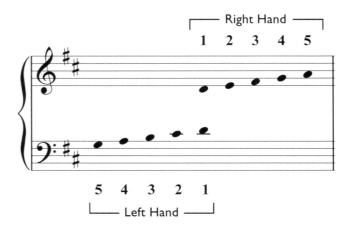

Smoothly and softly ♩ = 70

When you try your best but you don't suc - ceed,

when you get what you want but not what you need,

when you feel so tired but you can't sleep,

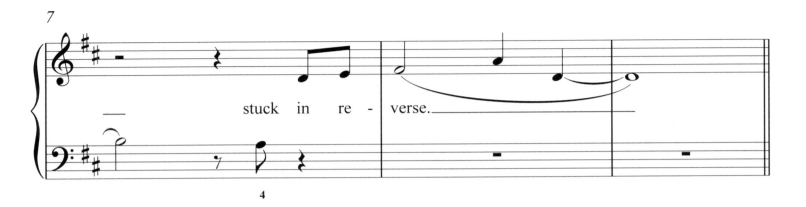

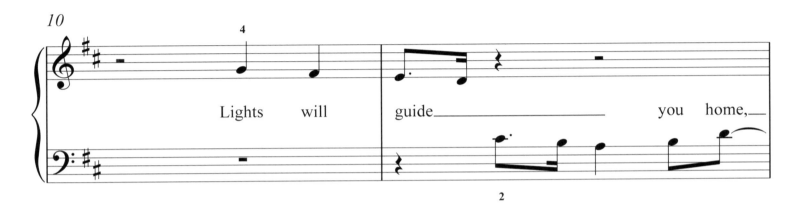

LEAVE RIGHT NOW

Words & Music by Francis White

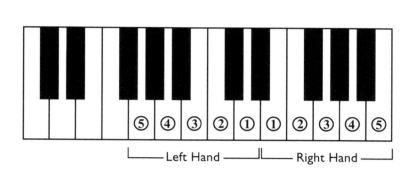

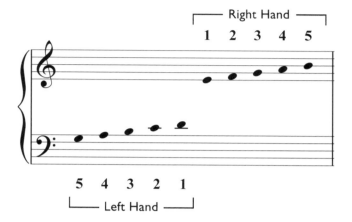

Expressively ♩ = 69

I'm here,_____ just like I said, though it's

break-ing ev-'ry rule I've ev-er made. My ra-cing heart_____ is just the

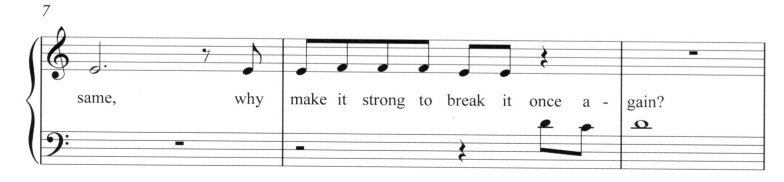

same, why make it strong to break it once a-gain?

LOVE ME TENDER

Words & Music by Elvis Presley & Vera Matson

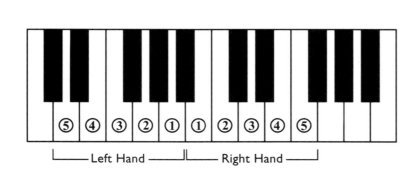

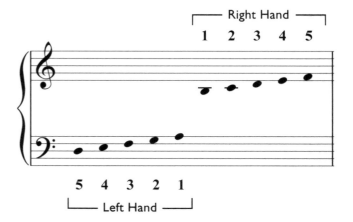

Love me ten-der, love me sweet, nev - er let me

go. You have made my life com-plete, and I love you so.

Love me ten-der, love me true, all my dreams, ful-fill.

IMAGINE

Words & Music by John Lennon

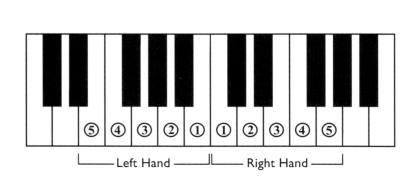

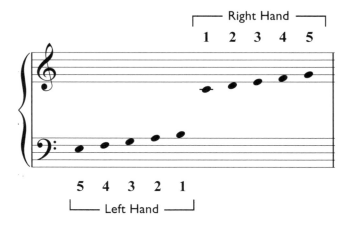

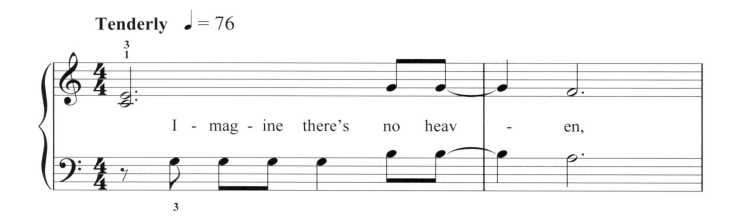

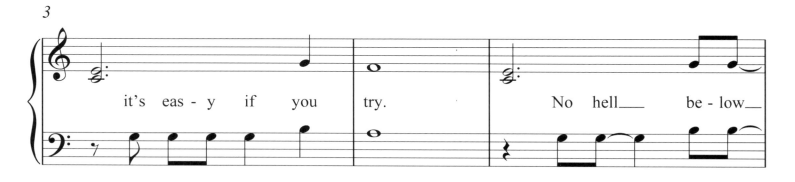

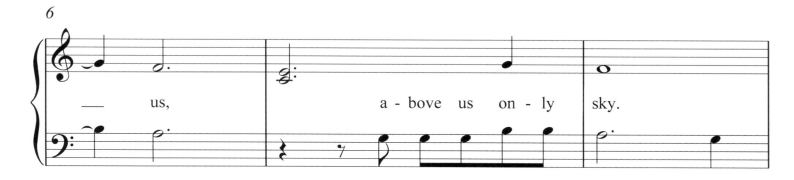

EVERY BREATH YOU TAKE

Words & Music by Sting

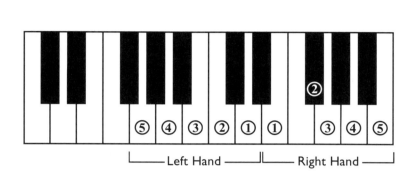

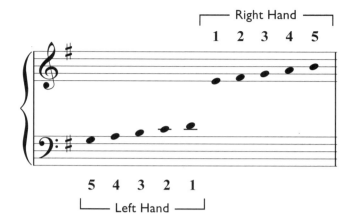

Softly ♩ = 112

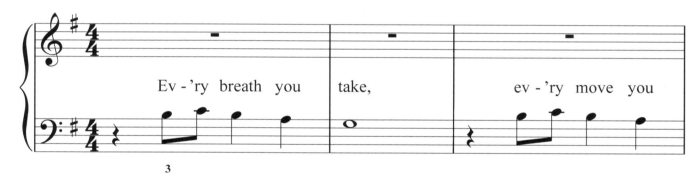

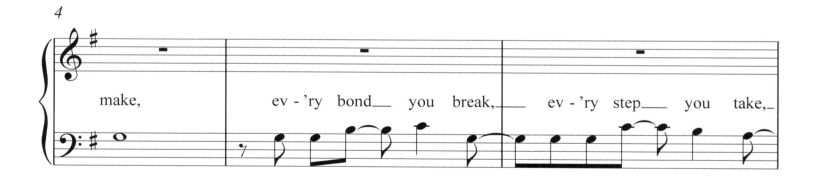

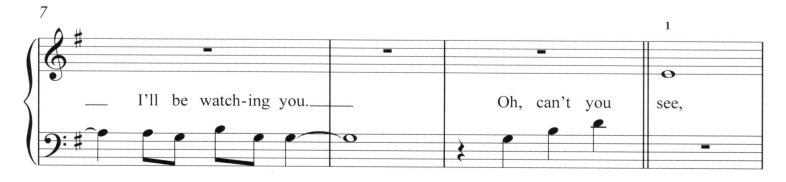

GEORGIA ON MY MIND

Words by Stuart Gorrell. Music by Hoagy Carmichael

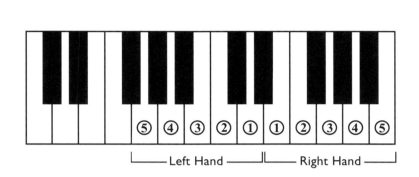

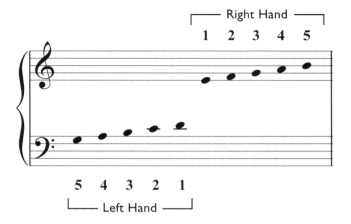

Geor - gia,   Geor - gia,   the whole day

through, just an old, sweet song keeps Geor - gia on my mind,

Geor-gia on my mind.   Geor-gia,   Geor - gia,   no peace I

SHE'S THE ONE

Words & Music by Karl Wallinger

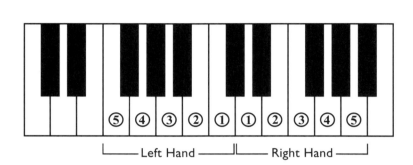

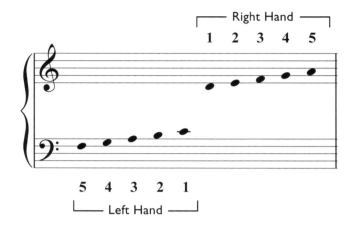

With feeling ♩ = 84

I was her,____ she was me.____

____ We were one,____ we were free. And if there's some-bod-

-y call-ing me on,____ she's the one.____

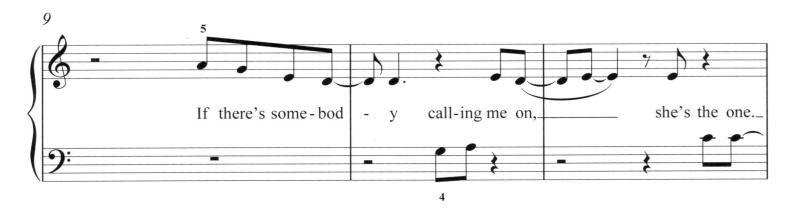

If there's some-bod - y call-ing me on, she's the one.

We were young, we were wrong.

We were fine, all a-long. And if there's some-bod-

- y call-ing me on, she's the one.

EASIEST 5-FINGER PIANO COLLECTION

ALSO AVAILABLE IN THE SERIES!

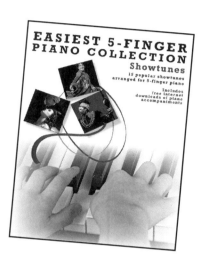

Chart Hits
15 popular chart hits including 'About You Now', 'Bleeding Love', 'Clocks', 'Foundations', 'Shine' and 'Umbrella'.
AM995357

Film Songs
15 great film songs including 'Breaking Free', 'Don't Worry, Be Happy', 'Somewhere Out There' and 'You've Got A Friend In Me'.
AM995335

Showtunes
15 great showtunes including 'Any Dream Will Do', 'Circle Of Life', 'Mamma Mia' and 'My Favourite Things'.
AM995324

Download to your computer a set of piano accompaniments for this *Ballads* edition
(to be played by a teacher/parent).
Visit: **www.hybridpublications.com**
Registration is free and easy.

Your registration code is RE651

Published by
Wise Publications
14-15 Berners Street,
London W1T 3LJ, UK.

Exclusive Distributors:
Music Sales Limited
Distribution Centre, Newmarket Road,
Bury St Edmunds, Suffolk IP33 3YB, UK.
Music Sales Pty Limited
20 Resolution Drive, Caringbah,
NSW 2229, Australia.

Order No. AM995346
ISBN 978-1-84772-726-8

Edited by Fiona Bolton.
Arranged and engraved by Camden Music.

Printed in the EU.

Your Guarantee of Quality
As publishers, we strive to produce every book to the highest commercial standards. This book has been carefully designed to minimise awkward page turns and to make playing from it a real pleasure. Particular care has been given to specifying acid-free, neutral-sized paper made from pulps which have not been elemental chlorine bleached. This pulp is from farmed sustainable forests and was produced with special regard for the environment. Throughout, the printing and binding have been planned to ensure a sturdy, attractive publication which should give years of enjoyment. If your copy fails to meet our high standards, please inform us and we will gladly replace it.

www.musicsales.com